CLASSIC LANDFORMS OF THE

BURREN
KARST

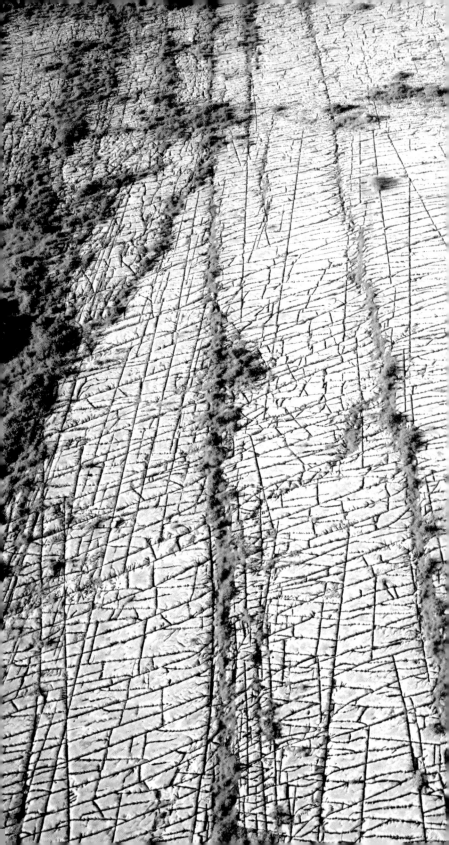

CLASSIC LANDFORMS OF THE
BURREN KARST

DAVID DREW
Trinity College Dublin

Series editors
Christopher Green, Michael Naish
and Sally Naish

Published by the Geographical Association
in conjunction with the
British Geomorphological Research Group

Geographical
Association

THE BRITISH GEOMORPHOLOGICAL RESEARCH GROUP

PREFACE

Geomorphologists study landforms and the processes that create and modify them. The results of their work, published as they invariably are in specialist journals, usually remain inaccessible to the general public. We should like to put that right. Scattered across the landscapes of England, Wales, Scotland and Ireland there are many beautiful and striking landforms which delight the eye of the general public and are also visited by educational parties from schools, colleges and universities. Our aim in producing this series of guides is to make modern explanations of these classic landforms available to all, in a style and format that will be easy to use in the field. We hope that an informed understanding of the origins of the features will help the visitor to enjoy the landscape all the more.

Encouraged by the success of the first edition of the Classic Landform Guides we are pleased to introduce this new title, enhanced by colour photographs and colour illustrations. The relevant maps for the area covered in this book are Ordnance Survey of Ireland *Discovery Series* 1:50,000 sheets 51 and 52 (Clare Galway), the 1:126,720 topographic sheet 14 and the 1:100,000 geology sheet 14.

Christopher Green *Royal Holloway, University of London*
Michael Naish and Sally Naish *Hayes, Kent*

Help

The Burren National Park covers the south eastern section of The Burren and the adjacent lowland. The National Park office is located at 2 Riverview, Corofin (Tel: 065 683 7166).

CONTENTS

Cover photograph: The bare slopes of Moneen Mountain. *Photo:* David Drew.
tispiece: The central portion of the Sheshymore limestone pavement in the south-central
Burren, looking south. *Photo:* David Drew.

Acknowledgements
The author wishes to thank Ken Blackmore, Sheila McMorrow and Terence Dunne of
Geography Department, Trinity College Dublin, for their cartographic and photographic
to this guide. Thanks are also due to Professor Adrian Phillips of the Geology Department,
Trinity College Dublin, for generating the satellite photograph of the area.
Geographical Association wishes to thank the Ordnance Survey Ireland for permission to
reproduce an extract from sheet 51 of the *Discovery Series* on the front cover.
act from Ordnance Survey Ireland © Government of Ireland Permit Number MP000101.
Copy Editing: Rose Pipes. *Illustrations:* Paul Coles
Series design concept: Quarto Design, Huddersfield
Design and typesetting: ATG Design, Catalyst Creative Imaging, Leeds
Printing and binding: Colorcraft Limited, Hong Kong

INTRODUCTION

The Burren plateau of north-west County Clare is the finest example of a **karstic** terrain in Ireland, with a full assemblage of the curious landforms and subterranean drainage systems that characterise such limestone regions. The landforms of The Burren have been strongly influenced by glacial and periglacial processes as well as by purely solutional karstic processes and in this respect the landscape more closely resembles that of the Yorkshire Dales or the upland **karsts** of counties Fermanagh, Sligo and Leitrim rather than unglaciated karsts such as the Mendip Hills. However, the internationally recognised significance of The Burren is also related to the remarkable flora of the region and to its rich archaeological heritage.

The Burren is bounded to the west by the Atlantic Ocean and to the north by Galway Bay (Figure 1 and Photo 1). The southern boundary may be defined geologically as the southern extremity of the outcrop of the limestone where it passes beneath younger rocks composed of shale and mudstone of Namurian age. This corresponds to an east to

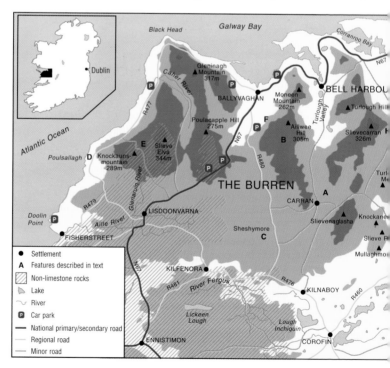

Table 1: The geological succession in the Burren.

Age	Formation	Member/Unit	Thickness	Lithological Characteristics	Associated Landforms	Associated Hydrological Features
NAMURIAN	Clare Shales		0m	Shales, mudstones and sandstones	Gentle slopes with slumping, rivers have incised gorges	Largely impermeable but with small springs at the limestone contact
BRIGANTIAN	Slievenaglasha Limestone		100m	Clean, coarse-grained limestone with chert bands and silicious fossiliferous horizons	Well developed limestone pavements near the top. Many enclosed depressions	Sinking streams and overflow springs at the shale contact. Springs associated with cherts near the base
ASBIAN	Burren Limestone	Aillwee	230m	Thick bedded with layers (wayboards) of shale between some beds	Cliff and terrace topography on northern flank. Fossil caves (e.g. Aillwee) above wayboards	Many small springs above the clay wayboards
ASBIAN	Burren Limestone	Maumcaha	320m	Massive limestone with no bedding and poorly developed jointing	Forms a distinctive straight slope beneath the terraced limestones	Springs at the top and at the base
HOLKERIAN		Fanore		Medium bedded with thin shale and chert layers	Extensive limestone pavements near to sea level	
HOLKERIAN		Ballard	470m	Fine grained with chert layers		Springs at Ballyvaghan, Bell Harbour and Corranroo Bay
ARUNDIAN	Tubber Limestone	Tubber		Fine to medium grained with shales, cherts and dolomites	Small caves above dolomite layer	Springs at contact with Burren Limestone

(Left margin vertical scale: 362.5 – 280 MYBP; 408 – 362 MYBP)

Note: The lithological characteristics of the various formations and members are summarised together with their associated landforms and hydrological features.

west line from Corofin through Kilfenora and Lisdoonvarna to the coast at Fisherstreet. The eastern limit of The Burren is the foot of the scarp at approximately 60m altitude which extends from Corranroo Bay in the north to Kilnaboy in the south-east. The area defined above is some 360km^2 in extent and forms a gently inclined plateau at 200-300m OD in the north and 50-150m OD in the south bounded by steep scarps on all but the southern flank. Only isolated summit areas exceed 300m in altitude and the highest point is the shale capped Slieve Elva at 344m OD. The lowlands of counties

Figure 1: Location and access to the Burren plateau and the adjacent Gort-Kinvarra lowlands. The features described in succeeding chapters are as follows: A: Carran depression; B: Aillwee Hill; C: Sheshymore limestone pavement; D: Poulsallagh coastal karren; E: Polldubh Cave; F: Aillwee Cave; G: Gort-Kinvarra lowland karst.

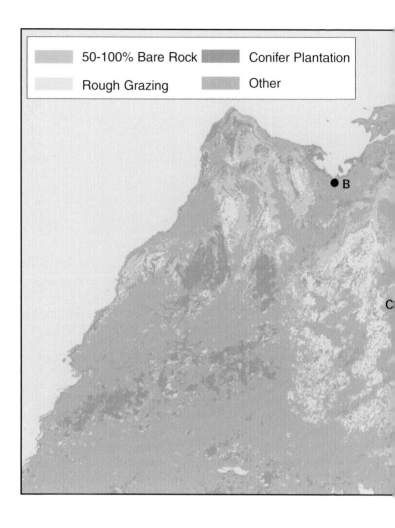

50-100% Bare Rock	Conifer Plantation
Rough Grazing	Other

Clare and Galway to the east of The Burren are also karstic landscapes and are briefly described in this guide. To the west, the three Aran Islands are an extension of the main Burren in many respects.

Following an overview of the geology, geomorphology and hydrology of the area, specific karst landforms, both surface and underground, are described together with a description of the karst of the nearby Gort-Kinvarra lowland.

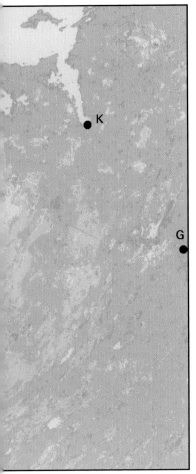

Photo 1: The Burren region. *On this false-colour satellite image, areas of limestone pavement with 50-100% bare rock are shown in orange, while rough grazing (areas with thin rendzina soils in most instances and probably areas of formerly bare rock) are shown yellow. The widespread occurrence of limestone pavement or partial pavement on the northern and eastern Burren is apparent. The area covered in the image is approximately that shown in Figure 1. Settlements – B: Ballyvaghan, C: Carran, G: Gort, K: Kinvarra.*

GEOLOGY AND LANDFORMS

The rocks

The Burren karst is developed in the Visean (Lower Carboniferous) limestones (Table 1) with some 500m of limestone succession being exposed. Two formations, the Slievenaglasha Limestone and Burren Limestone encompass the exposed strata on the upland. The Burren Limestone is subdivided into the Aillwee, Maumcaha, Fanore and Ballard members (Table 1). The differing characteristics of the limestones are reflected in landforms and in hydrology throughout The Burren (Table 1 and Figure 2). For example, the Maumcaha Member, which is 70m thick, with few joints or bedding planes, is overlain by a 140m thick strongly bedded sequence of limestones (the Aillwee Member) and underlain by a similar sequence some 150m thick. The massive member forms steep, uniform slopes or cliffs, while the bedded members form tiers of stepped terraces, particularly

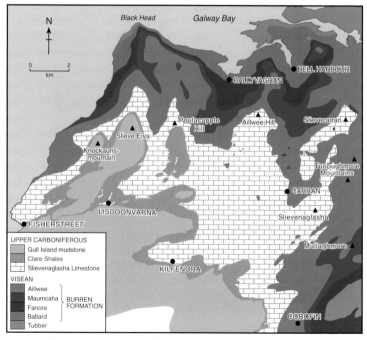

Figure 2: The bedrock geology of The Burren showing the outcrop of Namurian (shales and mudstone) and Visean (limestone) rocks. Adapted from: Geological Survey of Ireland mapping.

on the northern flank of The Burren overlooking the southern side of Galway Bay. The bedded limestones include both minor (5-15mm thick) and major (<600mm thick) shale layers called wayboards between certain beds and in many instances this shale layer provides a major obstacle to the vertical percolation of rainfall, forcing the water to flow sub-horizontally above the shale thereby developing cave systems and springs at this level in the limestones.

The uppermost part of the Carboniferous limestone is the Brigantian (Slievenaglasha Formation), characterised by more coarse-grained rocks than the Burren Limestone and incorporating numerous nodules or sheets of **chert** between beds of limestone. The chert seems to function in a similar manner to the shale layers as an important control on the groundwater movement and, to an extent, on landform development. The Slievenaglasha Limestone is susceptible to the processes of mechanical weathering and hence provides the mineral-grain skeleton for better developed **rendzina** soils than are found on the mechanically more resistant Burren Limestone.

Photo 2 shows the part of the limestone succession which is exposed on the western flank of Aillwee Hill to the south of Ballyvaghan and illustrates the topographical expression of some of the different limestones shown in Table 1.

Photo 2: The eastern side of the Ballyvaghan Valley, northern Burren. *Lithological differences determine the form of the valley-side slope. The straight slope to the valley floor comprises the massive Maumcaha Member. Above are the terraced limestones of the Aillwee Member with terraces occurring where layers of shale interrupt the limestone succession. The uppermost part of the hill is developed in the Slievenaglasha Limestone and does not exhibit terracing. The Ballyvaghan Valley is floored with till. Photo: David Drew.*

Resting on the Brigantian strata (Slievenaglasha Limestone) are the Namurian strata – the basal shales of which grade upwards into a sequence of shales, mudstones and sandstones. In the western Burren the Namurian rocks project northwards to form the uppermost part of the hills of Slieve Elva and Knockaunsmountain while the adjacent hill of Poulacapple is capped with a thin outlier of Namurian (Clare) shales.

Folds, faults and joints

The Burren area was at the extreme northern margin of the regions affected by mountain building at the end of Carboniferous times. The Carboniferous rocks of The Burren are tilted to the south-south-west with dips of 1-5° over much of the area; gentle asymmetric folding along north-north-east to south-south-west axes only becomes apparent in the eastern Burren. In this area are numerous asymmetrical small gorges or trenches developed along the axes of monoclinal folds. Typically one wall is a cliff and the other a more gentle slope. On a larger scale the folding of the strata is faithfully reflected in the morphology of hills such as Mullaghmore (Photo 3) and Slieve Roe.

Two major joint sets, oriented approximately north to south and east to west, occur over the whole area, their relative dominance and spacing varying locally. Faults are uncommon and fault-induced fractures are often **calcite** filled or associated with mineralisation.

Photo 3: The assymmetrically folded limestone strata in the extreme south-east of The Burren are reflected in the morphology of isolated hills such as Mullaghmore. Photo: David Drew.

Photo 4: The sink of the Glenaruin River near Lisdoonvarna. *The swallow hole just before the road, abandoned dry valley and other karstic features associated with the contact zone between the limestone and the overlying non-calcareous rocks are also apparent. Photo: David Drew.*

Karst development (**karstification**)

The slight inclination of the rocks over most of the Burren plateau forms an extensive dip-slope mainly of Slievenaglasha Limestone, declining gradually in altitude from north to south and contrasting with the steep north-facing scarp slope.

The karst of The Burren has developed as the overlying Namurian strata have been stripped away by fluvial and glacial action, exposing the limestone to solutional erosion. In the past, as now, the contact between the acidic impermeable Namurian rocks with surface rivers, and the limestone, was a zone of intense karstification. To the east of The Burren the contact between the older Devonian sandstones of Slieve Aughty and the limestone provides a similar focus for the development of underground drainage. In the long-term evolution of the Burren karst, surface drainage systems on the Namurian rocks firstly incised their valley floors to the underlying limestone. Drainage then became subterranean, as is beginning to happen with the Aille River system in the western Burren at present. Removal of the Namurian strata has extended westwards and southwards and thus the oldest karsts are those of the Gort-Kinvarra area while the youngest are those at the present shale-limestone contact in the Lisdoonvarna-Kilfenora area. Removal of the overlying rocks would have been uneven, with limestone windows being exposed in hollows in the Namurian rocks, so forming large enclosed depressions such as that at Carran and with islands of shale remaining surrounded by limestone, for example until recently on Slievecarran and Slievenaglasha hills. Such features may be seen at the present-day limestone-shale boundary. For example, Poulacapple Hill is an outlier of the Namurian strata with its surface drainage system progressively being directed underground as streams cut down to the underlying limestone around the margins. Photo 4 shows the present-day **sink** of the Glenaruin River into an exposure of limestone in its bed. Beyond, the now **dry valley** has decayed into **dolines** and a karst window surrounded by shales is developing into a large enclosed depression of the type described on pages 17-24. Such sequences of landforms associated with sinking streams may be found at many locations close to the geological boundary.

Glaciation

The Burren region was glaciated on at least two occasions during the Pleistocene Ice Age and many of its 'karstic' landforms must have been modified by cold climate processes. Significant accumulations of glacial deposits are now confined to the periphery of the area and to the floors of some large dolines. However, the extensive fields of glacially transported boulders (e.g. at Fanore M139081 – see Photo 5) and the accumulations of sediment in caves such as Glencurran (R 273964) near Carran may mean that a more extensive cover of glacial materials on the plateau has been largely eroded and washed underground. Fluvioglacial deposits occur along the eastern flank of The Burren, and glacial deposits in the valley of the River Fergus, on the lowlands to the east and in the major embayments (e.g. Ballyvaghan, Bell Harbour) and valleys (e.g. the Caher Valley).

The effects of glacial erosion, particularly the last ice advance, are apparent on the north-facing scarp, overlooking Galway Bay where a uniform ice-smoothed slope rises from sea-level to the plateau summit irrespective of lithological differences (front cover photograph). However, where ice moved parallel to the scarp as for example in the Ballyvaghan and Bell Harbour-Turlough valleys, lithological differences have been accentuated on the west and east facing valley sides. The ice removed the beds of weathered rock above the clay wayboards of the Aillwee Member, creating the distinctive cliff-and-terrace topography of the hillsides. The equivalent landforms on the plateau itself are the **limestone pavements**, though these are developed on all types of limestone.

The direction of at least the last ice advance approximately paralleled the orientation of the major joint set, north to south over much of The Burren. Many enclosed depressions are elongated along this axis, presumably as a result of additional glacial erosion by ice (e.g. on Aillwee Hill), while valleys such as Glencolumbkille (M 325005) in the east have been deepened and widened, so isolating the

Photo 5: At Fanore on the Burren coast glacially transported blocks of limestone rest on pedestals of bedrock. The underlying bedrock has been protected from solutional erosion for the past 12,000 years. Typical pedestal heights range from 400-600mm suggesting an average rate of lowering of the limestone surface of c. 0.04mm per year. Photo: David Drew.

rampart-like hills such as Knockanes (R 329974) and Turloughmore (R 338998 to M 340020) which form the eastern margin of The Burren. The embayments into the plateau at Ballyvaghan and Bell Harbour on the northern flank may also have been considerably modified by ice action.

Hydrology

The major hydrological features of The Burren are shown in Figure 3. Significant surface drainage on the limestone is confined to three short spring-fed streams flowing generally northwards (up-dip) but all of these streams cease to flow in dry weather. Underground drainage is strongly influenced by the geology. Chert and shale layers interbedded with the limestones make vertical percolation of water difficult and bedding partings offer much easier and laterally very extensive flow routes. Most of the stream cave passages that have been explored are developed above a layer of chert or shale and follow a single bed of limestone down-dip for considerable distances. The dip of the strata is generally to the south-south-west and this is also the direction of most groundwater flow. At the southern margin of The Burren the River Fergus flows westwards along the strike of the strata where the limestone dips beneath the Namurian rocks. The shales form the steep southern flank of the valley between Kilfenora and Corofin (Figure 2). The Fergus Valley is the local base level for groundwater with flow in

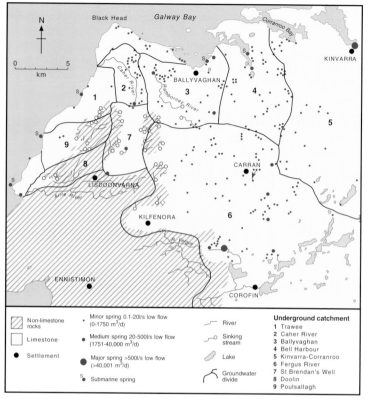

Figure 3: The Burren hydrology: surface drainage, sinking streams, springs and underground catchment divides.

the river being augmented by flows from numerous springs such as those at Roughaun (R 252923) and at Elmvale (R 257917) in the 4km reach of the River Fergus upstream of Inchiquin Lough. Approximately 40% of The Burren drains to these outlets.

St Brendan's Well spring (R 149987) near Lisdoonvarna is fed mainly by small streams which sink underground at the limestone-shale contacts of eastern Slieve Elva and western Poulacapple to the north. St Brendan's is located where the limestone dips beneath the Clare Shale (Figure 3) and water is thus forced to the surface as an overflow spring. The other major springs are along the Galway Bay and Atlantic shores of The Burren with some being in the inter-tidal zone and some being wholly submarine in location.

In addition there are numerous small, often intermittent springs throughout The Burren. Typically these are seepages of water from a bedding plane underlain by shale or chert with the water emerging where the bedding plane intersects the land surface at the base of a cliff or the side of a doline or valley. The water usually sinks underground within a few metres, en-route to one of the major peripheral springs.

ENCLOSED DEPRESSIONS

Enclosed drainage basins (dolines, **uvalas, poljes**) are characteristic of mature karst landscapes, functioning to concentrate runoff into the underground drainage network. More than 1500 enclosed depressions exceeding 100m^2 in floor area occur on the Burren plateau, together with several hundred smaller hollows. One-third of the depressions exceed 1000m^2 in area. The distribution of the depressions exceeding 100m^2 in floor area is shown in Figure 4 together with the outcrop of limestone and Namurian strata. The depressions are shown as a single dot irrespective of their actual dimensions. The greatest concentrations of enclosed depressions are in the central and eastern parts of the plateau with a smaller clustering between the Slieve Elva-Knockaunsmountain group and the coast (M 1002). Depressions are less frequent in the north of The Burren where slopes are steeper, and also in the vicinity of the contact between the limestones and the overlying non-calcareous rocks. This latter distribution may be due to the fact that dolines are a feature of a mature karst landscape. The Burren has become karstified as the removal of the Namurian rocks exposed the underlying limestone to karstic processes. Those areas furthest from the present-day

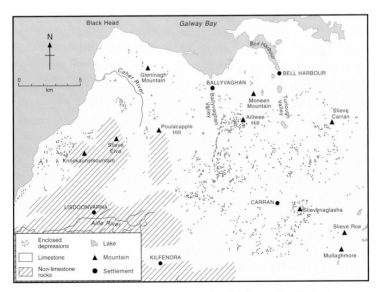

Figure 4: The distribution of enclosed depressions (dolines and uvalas) on the Burren plateau. The location of each depression is shown, not its extent.

Namurian rock outcrops will therefore have experienced karstification for the longest period of time.

Only one-quarter of the enclosed depressions are circular in form, the remainder being elongate to some extent with some 15% resembling sections of gorge or trench rather than conventional dolines. The elongation is commonly north-north-east to south-south-west and this seems to relate to the occurrence of a locally significant third joint set oriented north-east to south-west. Only some of the smaller depressions are oriented along the north to south joints. On the southern slope of Slievenaglasha Hill south of Carran (R 2796) is a system of steep-sided, flat-floored dry valleys trending to the south-south-west and largely undissected into dolines. Strongly oriented depressions are most common to the west of Knockaunsmountain, in the south-eastern Burren (south of Carran), and on the flanks of Aillwee Hill (described below). The dominant orientation of the enclosed depressions is parallel or sub-parallel to the direction of ice movement during the last glacial advance of the Pleistocene and glacial erosion may have enlarged many depressions and accentuated their elongation.

Karst landforms of Aillwee Hill

Aillwee Hill together with its northern extension, Moneen Mountain, is a northern salient of the Burren plateau, bounded to the west and the east by the Ballyvaghan and Bell Harbour-Turlough valleys respectively at 10-20m asl. The highest elevation, at 305m, lies just to the south of the scarp face overlooking Galway Bay. The northern, eastern and western flanks of the hill are developed in the Burren Limestone, mainly the terraced Aillwee Member. However, the main plateau surface is underlain by the overlying Slievenaglasha Limestone with the exception of small windows floored by Burren Limestone; for example the Glensleade depression (M 229011), the large uvala (Photo 6) near the summit (M 251048) and the Garracloon dry valley (M 241025). The area is located on the underground watershed between drainage north to Galway Bay and drainage south to the valley of the River Fergus.

The southern flank of the hill is located on the dip slope of the strata, the rocks dipping at 2-4° to the south-south-west to the contact with the overlying Namurian shales 11km distant. As elsewhere in The Burren the dominant joint set is oriented at 016° with secondary joint sets at 045 and 090°.

The gently sloping hillside is dissected by a series of discontinuous valleys, fragments of valleys and enclosed depressions, typically 20-50m in length and 5-20m in depth, the most significant of which are shown in Figure 5. The features converge on the large enclosed depression (area 1.5km², depth 30m) of Glensleade (M 229012) in the south-west. The most south-easterly of the features, in Ballymihill (M 247009), has the most complete valley form with steep, cliffed walls and a flat floor. The most westerly sequence is a linear chain of elongate dolines, oriented north to south and extending over the

Photo 6: Large and small dolines on the summit plateau of Aillwee Hill. *The major depression is oriented north-north-east to south-south-west while the smaller dolines and grooves are oriented north to south, paralleling the direction of the major joint set in the area. Photo: David Drew.*

shoulder of the hill, each doline being separated by a col from the next.

These landforms display the disintegration of a fluvial valley system into a karst drainage system of enclosed drainage basins and together comprise the densest concentration of mature karstic landforms in Ireland.

Some 600m south-west of the summit of Aillwee Hill and extending for 800m is a spectacular sequence of depressions-within-depressions (M 252048 to M 245042). The most southerly depression forms a steep-sided trench. Springs at the southern end form a stream which flows northwards (up-dip) before sinking underground after a surface course of 300m. The water reappears from springs in Ballyvaghan Bay (Figure 3). Glacial till deposits occur in the majority of the larger depressions and in the case of this large feature erratics of sandstone and of Connemara Granite are common. The most northerly and the deepest depression has a compound, uvala, form. A rock ridge extending across part of the floor is honeycombed with a network of cave passages which form a grid system (Figure 6a). The relict caves (Maze Holes, M 245048) (Photo 7) have circular or oval passage

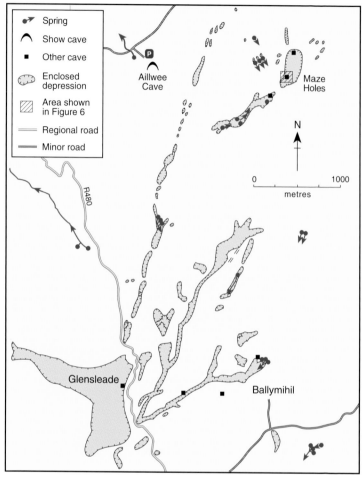

Figure 5: Karstic landforms on the southern (dip) slope of Aillwee Hill, *north-central Burren. A complex of oriented enclosed depressions, grooves, dry valleys and gorges pits the plateau surface. Abandoned (dry) caves are also shown.*

forms 1-2m in diameter suggesting that they were formed under water-filled (**phreatic**) conditions. As the present-day water table is close to sea-level and the caves are at an altitude of 245m, they must represent very ancient drainage features formed under very different topographic and hydrological conditions from those of today. Rounded erratics of sandstone are found on the floor in some of the passages (Figure 6b). Other small caves occur in the walls and headwalls of the Aillwee depressions and hence pre-date the formation of the depressions. The caves are all hydrologically inactive and seem to have become so when the depressions or valleys were excavated. Numerous springs and sinks occur in the enclosed depressions but seem to be segments of immature, probably post-glacial, drainage systems.

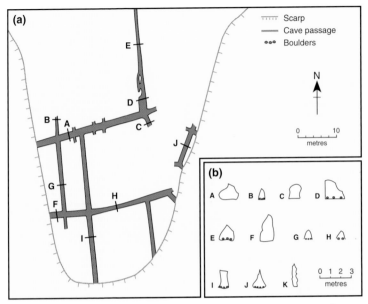

Figure 6: Maze Holes, a rectilinear network of relict caves near the summit of Aillwee Hill: (a) plan survey, and (b) passage cross-sections.

Photo 7: Two of the entrances to Maze Hole caves developed in a spur within the uvala on Aillwee Hill. Photo: David Drew.

The Kilcorney-Meggagh and Carran enclosed depressions

To the south and south-east of Aillwee Hill are two very large enclosed basins, sufficiently large to be described as poljes or large uvalas (compound enclosed depressions), with a combined area of $c.$ 16km^2 enclosed by the 125m OD contour. Figure 7 shows the morphology and features of these two enclosed depressions. The Carran depression has an area of 9km^2 and extends to an average depth of 30m below the surrounding plateau surface (Photo 8a). It is flat-floored and has steep surrounding slopes. The south-western and north-eastern extremities of the basin are blocked to some degree by till deposits. The Castletown River fed by springs in the northern part of the Carran depression meanders across the floor of the basin before sinking underground (R 294980) near Castletown on the southern side. The waters drain to springs in the valley of the River Fergus some 6km to the south. In wet conditions the **swallow holes** are unable to cope with the inflow of water and lakes form in the depression (Photo 8b), even though the floor of the basin is more than 70m above the water table.

To the west of the Carran depression is the slightly smaller enclosed basin of Kilcorney-Meggagh with a total floor area of 7km^2 (Figure 7). This includes two distinct deep hollows embedded in a more extensive area of internal drainage. These depressions may be genetically linked to the features on Aillwee Hill described on pages 17-21. Both hollows flood to some extent in wet weather, the waters at Kilcorney emerging under considerable pressure from the floor of the depression near its lowest elevation. In the same part of the Kilcorney depression is a series of caves opposite one another in the

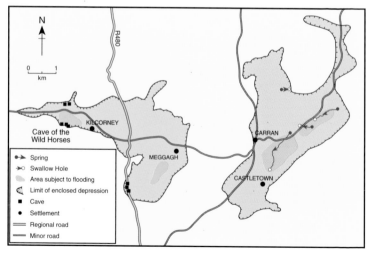

Figure 7: The enclosed depressions of Kilcorney-Meggagh and Carran: *present-day hydrology and inactive caves.*

Photo 8: The Carran depression under: (a) low water conditions, and (b) wet conditions. Photos: David Drew.

cliffs of the north (R 225998) and south (R 223992) sides of the depression. The caves seem to comprise a series of high-level ancient conduits running from north to south (down-dip) which have been bisected by the development of the younger Kilcorney depression. Only the lowest of these caves, the Cave of the Wild Horses (R 223992), on the southern side is hydrologically active and even then only when that part of the depression floods.

The floors of the Carran and Kilcorney-Meggagh depressions are at similar altitudes (85-100m) though the depth of the infilling sediment is unknown. In each instance, although the depression is formed in the uppermost Slievenaglasha Limestone, the floor reaches the underlying Burren Limestone – a zone characterised by an abundance of silicified limestones which may have proved a barrier to further deepening. The Carran and Meggagh depressions are both oriented north-north-east to south-south-west, a dominant trend for valleys and enclosed depressions over much of the Burren. However, the Kilcorney depression shows a marked east to west orientation with its western extremity having a valley or gorge-like form and extending almost as far as the boundary with the Namurian rocks at R 201993.

Unlike polje features in other karst regions, these large enclosed basins do not seem to be significantly controlled by tectonic or lithological factors. It may be that they developed as exposures of limestone (karst windows) at a time when the limestones of the remainder of the plateau were overlain by impermeable Namurian rocks. This hypothesis is supported by the fact that the plateau to the south of the basins is composed of the uppermost beds of the Carboniferous limestone.

Access

The R480 between Ballyvaghan and Leamaneh Castle traverses the western side of Aillwee Hill. The easiest access to the summit area (walkers with permission only – from Ballyallaban House) is via the gated farm road at Berneens (M 230024).

Some 3km further south on the R480 and passing many dolines and segments of dry valleys en-route, the road descends into the eastern part of the Kilcorney depression at Ballydoora crossroads (R 238989). West from the junction, a minor road runs through the centre of the Kilcorney depression for 3km. East from the crossroads the minor road crosses the deep Meggagh depression and then leads to the south-western margin of the Carran polje via an excellent viewpoint at Ballyconry (R 277986).

LIMESTONE PAVEMENT AT SHESHYMORE

Limestone pavements or decayed pavements with surfaces of loose limestone slabs cover 20% of the Burren plateau and its northern flank. A further 30% of the plateau surface consists of a mosaic of bare rock and patches of thin rendzina soils (Photo 1, pages 8-9). The pavements are presumed to be the product of the removal of soil, broken rock and non-coherent bedrock by glacial erosion leaving a bare, unkarstified rock surface. The best pavements develop where the dip of the rocks is low and where the dip of the rocks corresponds to the slope of the ground surface. Both of these conditions pertain over much of the Burren plateau.

Limestone pavements are found on all the limestones of The Burren but are particularly well developed on the highest beds of the Brigantian, near the contact with the Namurian strata. Extensive limestone pavements occur near the coast at Oughtdarra (M 095023), to the north of Slieve Elva and Poulacapple Hill, on folded strata in the south-eastern Burren at Mullaghmore (R 327954), on isolated hills on the eastern ramparts of The Burren at Doomore (M 315024) and Turloughmore (M 337007), and on the lowlands between The Burren and Gort, for example at R 345955, west of Rockforest Lough. The general distribution of limestone pavements and of other areas of bare rock are apparent in Photo 1 (pages 8-9)

One of the finest and most intact areas of pavement is at Sheshymore (see Frontispiece, page 2) to the south of Carran in the south-central Burren (R 239961). The pavement extends over an area of 33ha, degraded and overgrown on its periphery but including a central core of 11ha of almost perfectly intact pavement. The limestone pavement is developed on a single bed of Brigantian Formation (Slievenaglasha Limestone) within a shallow syncline (dips of 2°) oriented north-east to south-west. To the east, north and south the land surface is developed on the underlying limestone bed and little or no pavement has developed or persisted. North to south and east to west joints are prevalent over the whole area. In the central and north-western part the east to west joints are spaced much more closely (1.2-1.5m) than the north to south joints (2-9m), hence the resulting **clint** blocks are rectangular (Photo 9). Elsewhere, transverse joints allow triangular clints to develop. Enlarged curved joints occur especially in the north-eastern part of the pavement. The enlarged joints (**grikes**) are commonly up to 800mm in width and 1-2m in depth. Some of the north to south joints traverse all or most of the pavement as a single fissure. These 'major' joints are usually vegetation filled and may

Photo 9: Close-up of the central part of the Sheshymore pavement *looking south and showing the dominant east to west joint set spaced 1-1.5m apart.* Photo: David Drew.

represent the main conduits for groundwater movement in the area towards the River Fergus to the south.

Although the grikes are well developed, **karren** development on the clint blocks is largely confined to the periphery of the area of pavement where there is a full range of karren forms including **kamenitza** (solutional pans), rundkarren (rounded runnels leading rainwater into the grikes) and, on gentler slopes, meandering runoff karren. In the core area of the pavement the clint blocks are almost wholly undissected by karren, suggesting that, until comparatively recently, the pavement may have been protected from solutional erosion by a blanket of calcareous till. Traces of such a mineral soil can be found at depth in some of the grikes, suggesting that it was eroded from the surface and washed underground.

The orientation of the main joint sets in the central part of the Sheshymore limestone pavement is shown in Figure 8. East to west oriented joints are common with a second set north to south and subsidiary joint sets oriented approximately north-west to south-east and north-east to south-west.

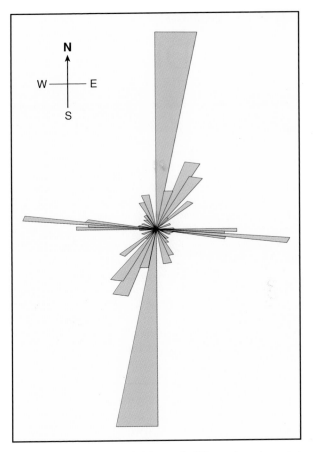

Figure 8: The orientation of the main joint sets in 5° intervals on the central part of the Sheshymore limestone pavement. After an original by B. McSharry, Trinity College Dublin.

Access

The Sheshymore limestone pavement is visible on the western side of the R480 Ballyvaghan to Leamaneh Castle road, some 2.5km south of the Ballydoora crossroads (Kilcorney enclosed depression, see pages 22-24) and 2.5km north of the Leamaneh Castle junction. Park in the layby some 500m north of the pavement.

COASTAL KARST LANDFORMS

Along much of the Burren coastline and especially on the western Atlantic-facing shore, limestone bedrock is exposed on the foreshore. Inland, limestone pavements are widespread, and on them solution of the limestone under sub-aerial conditions by rainwater is dominant. However, between high and low tide levels a distinctive suite of micro landforms of solutional origin (karren) has developed irrespective of the local limestone lithology or structure.

Sea-water is saturated with respect to calcium and magnesium carbonates and hence cannot dissolve significant quantities of limestone. However, the presence of life forms (micro and macro, fauna and flora) in the hollows in the rock in this littoral zone generates respired carbon dioxide which dissolves in the pool of trapped sea-water and slightly acidifies it. Solution of the limestone walls and floor of the pool can then occur at low tide. The water is replaced by the incoming tide and the cycle repeats twice daily. Many marine organisms also 'graze' the limestone surface while others

Photo 10: Poulsallagh foreshore: *At centre-left is the moraine which protects the underlying limestone from solutional erosion. In the foreground are typical sub-aerial karren forms while the top of the isolated rock at centre-right is dissected by typical littoral zone kamenitza. Photo: David Drew.*

28

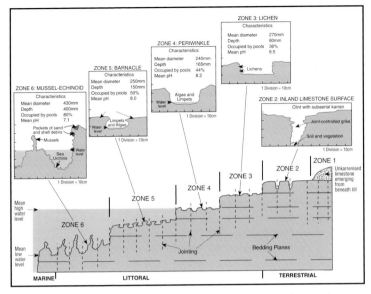

Figure 9: The littoral zone on the Poulsallagh foreshore *showing the zonation of karren forms between high and low tide levels, dominant life forms, mean physical characteristics of the kamenitza and chemistry of the water. Adapted from: Lundberg, 1997.*

excavate hollows or tubes into the rock thereby intensifying erosion of the rock in the pools. The density and variety of life forms increases towards low tide level and so therefore does carbon dioxide production and the intensity of erosion of the limestone.

Unlike on inland limestone pavements where joints are usually widened by solutional activity into grikes and form conspicuous features; in the inter-tidal zone joints are hard to discern and the dominant karren forms are the hollows called kamenitza. Such littoral zone karren occur over some 15km of coastline between Black Head (M 155122) and Doolin Point (R 060970). An easily accessible site is at Poulsallagh (M 085015). Between Poulsallagh Bay to the north and the small inlet of Cancapple Bay (M 085014) to the south a single bed of limestone, dipping gently to the south, exhibits a full sequence of karren forms (Figure 9). The same sequence of karren forms is developed in much more compact fashion on the succession of limestone beds separated by small cliffs, oriented east to west along the strike of the rocks. Poulsallagh is located in the Aillwee Member of the Burren Limestone.

An extensive area of hummocky moraine occurs on this part of the Burren coast. Marine erosion has winnowed the finer sediments from the moraine in the wave zone leaving large cobbles and boulders which have been partly re-worked into a storm beach (Photo 10). The calcareous material of the moraine has protected the underlying limestone from solutional erosion, and on the southern side of

Poulsallagh Bay smooth, uneroded limestone can be seen emerging from beneath the eroding till cover. Within a few metres of the till cover the limestone has been exposed to the erosive action of acidified rainwater sufficiently long enough for sub-aerial karren to have begun to develop. As the limestone bed is followed down-dip to the south into the littoral zone, so the dominant karren forms become kamenitza. Initially they consist of shallow flat pans on the smooth limestone surface but closer to low tide level the pools are wider and deeper with the intervening areas consisting of rock pinnacles and almost no level surfaces.

Six, somewhat arbitrary zones of karren development have been described, from inland to below the low tide mark. The relative locations of these zones, their characteristic morphology, dimensions and their life forms are shown in Figure 9. Photos 11a and 11b illustrate the Barnacle and Mussel-Echinoid zones respectively.

Photo 11: Poulsallagh foreshore zones: *(a) Zone 5 rounded pinnacles armoured with barnacles are separated by deep, hemispherical pools, and (b) close to low tide level in Zone 6, echinoids (sea-urchin) excavate individual pits in the floor of rock pools. Photos: David Drew.*

Access

From the N67 at Lisdoonvarna take the R477 north-west towards Black Head and follow the road onto the Atlantic coastline. Poulsallagh Bay is located where the R477 first reaches the coast at Ballyryan (M 087018). Check tide times, to ensure that your group can explore most of the zones on the foreshore. **If high seas prevail do not attempt to reach the foreshore, large waves make this and other sections of the Burren coast dangerous.**

THE CAVES OF THE BURREN

The caves of The Burren, in themselves a reflection of past and present hydrogeological conditions, have been controlled in their origin and evolution by three main factors:

1. Geological controls, in particular the dip of the rocks, the joint systems and the presence of relatively impermeable layers such as chert or shales within the limestone sequence.
2. Modification of karstic processes by other factors, for example, the effects of changes in base level, or the effects of glacial erosion and deposition.
3. The degree to which runoff is concentrated prior to sinking underground. Such concentration into streams occurs on the impermeable terrain of the Namurian strata in the west of The Burren.

Associated with these sinking streams is a series of river caves mainly developed in the north to south joint systems and oriented north to south down-dip. Such caves are commonly developed within a single bedding plane for long distances, occasionally stepping down one (bed) or more via a vertical drop. The vertical location of these cave conduits is often determined by the presence of chert-rich zones within the uppermost beds of the Slievenaglasha Limestones, which appear to constrain the vertical movement of water.

The passage form of these caves typically comprises a wide, low roof section of enlarged bedding plane incised by a narrow trench or canyon which contains the stream. The trench is typically 0.3-3m wide but may be up to 30m deep. Passage cross-sections are therefore typically T-shaped. The roof section of a passage is of phreatic origin (developed when the passage was completely water filled) while the trench has been cut under **vadose** (open water surface) conditions. Four types of stream cave may be recognised:

1. Simple, single stream conduits in which the morphology and dimensions of the cave passage are obviously related to the present-day stream, e.g. Polldubh (M 134032).
2. Stream caves with abandoned sections of passage, oxbows and offset meander belts at different heights above the active stream route. There is commonly appreciable deposition of calcite **speleothems** and deposits of fossil sediments derived from outside the cave, some of which are undergoing re-excavation. Pollnagollum (M 161038) and to some extent the Cullaun series of caves (e.g. Cullaun one, M 182023) are examples of this type.

3. Caves of the first two types which have intersected reaches of apparently much older, now fossil cave systems. Such 'older' caves are often characterised by a circular or oval passage cross-section suggesting a wholly phreatic origin and by extensive fill deposits. Faunarooska (M 143048) and Pollballiny (M 140043) caves are examples of polycyclic caves.

4. Caves of presumed great age which have been abandoned by the streams that formed them, e.g. Vigo Cave at Nooan (R 260900), Aillwee Cave (M 233048). Sediment infills are widespread in these caves, ranging in type from complex bedded sequences of fine sediments (e.g. Pol-an-Ionain Cave near Craggycorradan (R 101997) and Aillwee Cave) to extensive sand deposits of unknown origin as in Glencurran Cave south of Carran (R 273964).

The age of the Burren caves has not been thoroughly investigated but limited evidence from **uranium series dating** of calcite specimens suggests that the simple stream passage caves may be of Holocene age (i.e. formed during the last 10,000 years) while the more complex stream caves may originate from at least the last interglacial times (120-132,000 years ago).

Polldubh Cave, Slieve Elva

Polldubh Cave (M 134032), located on the western flank of Slieve Elva, is a good example of a simple stream cave related to present day-landforms and hydrology and very probably of Holocene age. As the plan survey (Figure 10a) shows, the cave passage is closely associated with the present day shale to limestone boundary, paralleling the boundary and functioning as a drain collecting water from the numerous stream sinks at the shale margin. Polldubh is an example of a simple **vadose cave** of relatively recent origin that is typical of many of the caves developed by sinking streams. The cave is developed in the north to south oriented joint system and follows the shallow (0-5°) dip to the south. The cave system is developed within the uppermost 2-10m of the Slievenaglasha Limestone and is therefore always within a few metres of the surface. The water re-appears at the surface a short distance beyond the limit of exploration in the cave and then flows south, sinking again into a very immature cave system. Under high flow conditions in this section the capacity of the cave passage is exceeded and a stream flows on the surface. Thus, all the stages of initiation and early development of karstic drainage are represented in the Polldubh system.

The main stream sink, Polldubh South, which feeds the Polldubh system, has created a series of small canyon passages less than 1m² in cross-sectional area, all of which unite into a single conduit some 2.6m high developed in four beds of limestone. The passage meanders gently with an amplitude of 15m. The phreatic roof bedding plane is *c.* 150mm high and contains flood-borne deposits. Further downstream the passage enlarges and the scalloping on the walls

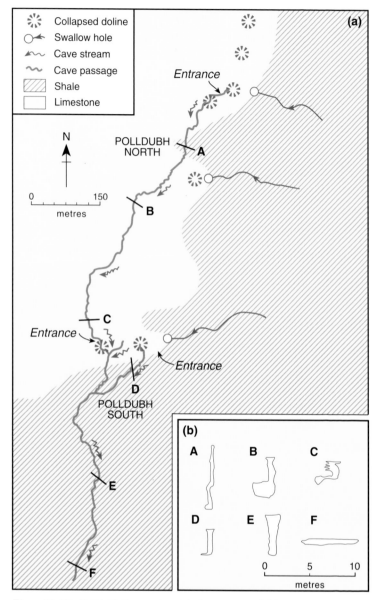

Figure 10: The Polldubh Cave system: *(a) plan survey, and (b) passage cross-sections A-F. The cave passage is depicted as a single line due to the small passage width compared to passage length. Adapted from: Self, 1981.*

increases in diameter from 10-20mm to 30-40mm corresponding to the reduction in stream velocity (Figure 10b). Evidence for a recent increase in stream discharge or velocity is provided by the patches of partly calcreted gravels that are now being eroded. The level of frequent and occasional floods can be determined by reference to the

Photo 12: The vadose canyon in Polldubh South Cave with the stream from Polldubh North entering from a higher level passage. The variations in scallop size on the passage walls reflect differences in the velocity of water flow. Photo: Terence Dunne.

zones of calcite deposition on the passage walls above the stream, there being no deposition in the lowest 500mm, and thick calcite deposits higher than 1m above the floor.

One hundred and twenty metres from the entrance, the water from Polldubh North enters Polldubh South at roof level – the passage being developed in the same bed as that in which the Polldubh South passage was initiated (Photo 12). The steepening of gradient associated with this junction has allowed the cave stream to cut through the chert layers above which the passage upstream is perched (cross-section D, Figure 10b). Further downstream the deep vadose canyon (cross-section E) diminishes in height until eventually the passage has no vadose component and is wholly developed in the bedding with a width of several metres and a height of only 250-300mm. This passage is still phreatic under wet weather conditions (cross-section F).

Polldubh North has a uniform cross-sectional area though height and width vary. Beyond the point at which Polldubh North passes out from beneath the shales, calcite deposition, mainly derived from seepages down north to south oriented joints, is extensive. A collapse to the surface at the intersection of solutionally enlarged cross joints forms an alternative entrance to the cave.

Aillwee Cave, Ballyvaghan

Aillwee Cave represents the opposite end of the spectrum of Burren caves to Polldubh in that it is an ancient system with a complex history which reflects environmental changes that took place on the surface above. The cave is located 3km south of Ballyvaghan on the western flank of Aillwee Hill at an altitude of 92m. The vertical location of Aillwee Cave is strongly influenced by lithology, just above the contact between the terraced Aillwee Member and the massive Maumcaha Member beneath. More significant controls are the presence of a thick shale band (wayboard) and 100-300mm above it, thick bands of calcite inter-bedded with the limestone. These layers are relatively impermeable to the vertical movement of water, and seepages and springs occur above them in many locations on The Burren. The shale and calcite layers also controlled the early stages of the evolution of Aillwee Cave, the oldest passages of which are excavated in the fossil-rich beds of limestone immediately above the calcite layer.

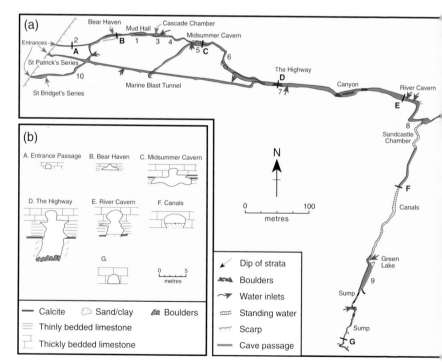

Figure 11: Aillwee Cave: (a) plan survey, and (b) passage cross-sections (looking into the cave). Specific locations referred to in the text are labelled 1-10.

As the survey (Figure 11a) shows, Aillwee Cave consists basically of a single tunnel. The first 500m of passage from the entrance is oriented west to east along the strike of the strata while the remainder of the cave is oriented down-dip, just west of south. A sharp bend at the River Cavern marks this change in direction. Close to the cliff face the main passage splits into a series of smaller tunnels, each with its own entrance at the base of the cliff.

Much of the past history of Aillwee Cave is preserved at various locations underground. The earliest stages in the development of the cave are represented by networks of small intersecting tubes (**anastomoses**), 40-250mm in diameter, which originated as water moved slowly along a bedding plane in the Aillwee Limestone. These anastomosing channels are now preserved in the roof at locations such as Mud Hall (1 on Figure 11a, see also Photo 13) and Midsummer Cavern (5) where the lower limestone bed has fallen away leaving the anastomoses visible on the flat roof. Eventually the water established a preferred, direct route, excavating a single tube which carried large volumes of water. The lower part of the tube has been destroyed by rock collapse, but the upper, **half tube**, remains, extending the full length of the cave and increasing in diameter from 900mm near the entrance (2) to 2200mm at the eastern extremity of the cave. The half tube is apparent in all the passage cross-sections in Figure 11b and Photo 14.

When the cave passage became vadose (having an air surface) solutional erosion became predominantly vertical and a canyon-like passage at least 20m deep was excavated. The form of this passage can be seen at locations such as The Highway (cross-section D, Figure 11b) and the River Cavern (cross section E).

Photo 13: Mud Hall, Aillwee Cave: *roof anastomoses at the base of the limestone bed above the shale wayboard layer. On the right anastomosing channels have been linked to form a continuous straight conduit. Photo: Terence Dunne.*

Photo 14: The half tube in the roof of Cascade Chamber, Aillwee Cave.
The bedding plane above which the half tube (upper right) was excavated is visible.
Photo: Terence Dunne.

Since this canyon was abandoned by the stream that formed it, the cave has gradually decayed. Block collapse of the roof and particularly of the side walls by spalling of large joint-bounded blocks, for example in Cascade Chamber (site 3 on Figure 11a), has destroyed much of the original passage form. Sediments of external origin were introduced into the cave during this decay phase. The outer passages of the cave as far as what was a complete blockage in the main passage 200m from the entrance, are characterised by a diamicton (poorly sorted deposit) fill of sand and cobbles in a clayey matrix (e.g. at sites 4 and 10, Figure 11a). This was almost certainly derived from the immediate vicinity of the cave. Beyond the former blockage the dominant sediments are rhythmites, alternating layers of sand, silt and clay deposited by running water. The rhythmites are well exposed in The Highway (site 7, Figure 11a) and beyond. Fluvial sands and gravels are also abundant in the further reaches of the cave (e.g. at sites 8 and 9, Figure 11a). The grain size of the sands increases from east to west into the cave while the carbonate content of the sand decreases from 85% to 70%. It is likely that glacial deposits on the surface were the original source for all of these deposits.

The most significant process modifying Aillwee Cave at present is removal of sediment and dissolution of collapsed blocks by seepages and streams which have invaded the passages. At some locations: The Highway, Cascade Chamber and River Cavern in particular, the removal of sediment and subsidence of breakdown material has been sufficient to reveal a large part of the former vadose passage. The present drainage in the cave is from east to west to springs at the base of the hill below the cave entrance. This represents a reversal of the west to east flow, into the hill, that originally developed the cave.

The age of Aillwee Cave is unknown, though uranium series dating of calcite deposits suggest the main passages had attained much of their present form more than 350,000 years ago. The cave's location, perched 100m above the floor of the Ballyvaghan Valley, means that the surrounding topography would need to have been very different during the cave's initiation and development. Calcite deposited on collapsed blocks was typically deposited episodically for periods of 1000-3000 years during the past 10,000 years. This suggests that block breakdown has been very limited during the Holocene.

Many of the features of early cave development, including incipient roof tubes, are intersected by the 300m-long Marine Blast tunnel which links St Bridget's Series with The Highway.

Safety and access

All of the caves described in this guide are in their natural state with the exception of Aillwee Cave, which is a commercial cave. **Caves should not be entered except by those with experience of caving and/or under expert supervision.** Most Burren stream caves flood rapidly following moderate to heavy rainfall and the river caves of the Gort-Kinvarra area contain hazardous sections of very deep water.

Polldubh Cave can be accessed from the west or the east via a minor road which crosses the upland between Knockaunsmountain and Slieve Elva and runs between the R477 and the N67. From the R477 take the minor road east from Fanore (M 134071) or join the same road by turning west on the N67 at R 153997. Park on the eastern side of this road, near its highest point (M 134035) and, on foot, follow the course of an overhead electricity transmission line south into the forestry through a clearing. From the second pylon in the forestry an ill-defined and very muddy track leads to the east through the trees for 250m to the entrance to Polldubh South.

Aillwee Cave is a show cave, located 3km south of Ballyvaghan close to the R480. It is extensively signposted from Ballyvaghan and the N67 and is served by a large car park at M 234049. The cave can be traversed safely along most of its length.

THE GORT-KINVARRA LOWLANDS

Between the Burren plateau to the west and the Devonian sandstone upland of Slieve Aughty to the east is a lowland corridor underlain by Carboniferous limestone. The lowland extends southwards to the River Fergus and the estuary of the River Shannon and northwards into the limestone lowlands of the eastern part of counties Galway and Mayo and much of County Roscommon, an area of more than 4000km², most of which is karstic to some degree. The portion of this lowland between the towns of Gort and Kinvarra is part of a drainage basin which has its outlets in coastal springs at Kinvarra (M 379103) and further west at Corranroo Bay (M 325105). The total catchment area for these springs is approximately 500km² of which 250km² is located on the Devonian rocks with elevations reaching 370m and with normal surface drainage systems. The other 250km², on limestone, is below 30m in elevation and has largely subterranean drainage. This area is a mature lowland karst landscape with landforms and hydrology that contrast sharply with the upland karst features of The Burren.

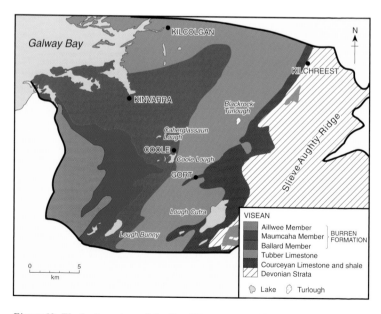

Figure 12: The basic geology of the Gort-Kinvarra area. Adapted from: Office of Public Works, 1997.

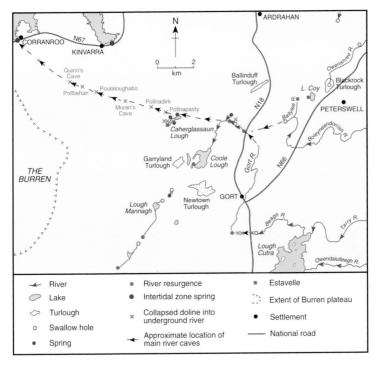

Figure 13: The hydrology and major karst features of the Gort-Kinvarra lowlands catchment which feeds the coastal springs at Kinvarra and Corranroo Bay.

The basic geology of the Gort-Kinvarra area is shown in Figure 12 and the drainage and major karst landforms in Figure 13. The bedrock comprises the lower part of the Carboniferous limestone succession with the limestones becoming generally less pure and less karstifiable towards the contact with the Devonian rocks. This lithological contact corresponds with the sharp break of slope at the foot of the north-east to south-west trending Slieve Aughty ridge to the east.

Three rivers drain the upland. From north to south they are the Owenshree, the Ballylee (Boleyneendorish) and the Owendalulleegh (Beagh/Gort River). After reaching the limestone these rivers flow parallel to the upland for some distance before sinking underground. They eventually re-appear from the coastal springs some 10-15km to the north-west at Kinvarra and Corranroo Bay. Three distinctive hydro-geomorphic karstic environments occur in this south-east to north-west transect:

1. the area of stream sinks,
2. the area of surface-water karst-water interaction and,
3. (closest to the coastal springs) an area of wholly underground drainage.

41

Sinking streams

The Owenshree River flows over the limestone in a south-westerly direction. In dry weather it sinks in its bed but more commonly continues into the large enclosed basin of Blackrock Turlough (Turloughnacloghdoo, M 580080) before sinking underground (Figure 14a). Following heavy rainfall this turlough becomes a lake almost 1km in diameter and 10m deep within 36 hours. Under these conditions some of this sinking water continues to flow underground to the south-west for 1km, some of it discharges under pressure from a spring (at M 490075) on the western shore of the smaller Lough Coy, and the remainder continues underground for a further 1km before emerging under great pressure as a spring (at M 482073) from the northern branch of the Ballylee River (Figure 14c). As water levels fall, the Lough Coy spring becomes a swallow hole, which engulfs the lake waters, while the northern Ballylee River site also reverses its flow and acts as a swallow hole instead of a spring. Both of these sites are estavelles (Figure 14b and c). As Figure 13 shows, the Ballyleee River has two branches, the more southerly of which always terminates in a swallow hole and the more northerly of which ends in what is a swallow hole only under medium and low water conditions and becomes a spring in times of heavy rainfall.

The most southerly of the sinking rivers, the Owendalulleegh/ Beagh/Gort, alternates surface and subterranean sections for 1.5km of its course downstream of Lough Cutra (see Figure 15). The first sink, one of the largest in Ireland, is at the end of a 15m deep gorge incised

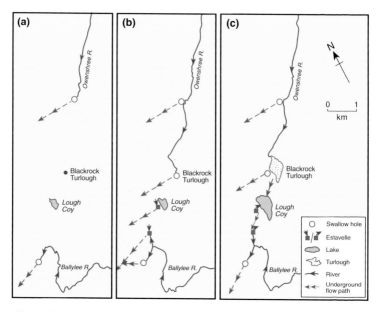

Figure 14: Underground and surface drainage of the Owenshree and Ballylee rivers under: (a) low, (b) medium and (c) high water conditions.

into till and the underlying cherty limestones (M 458002). A dry channel continues at a higher level from the sink into the large conical enclosed depression known as the Punch Bowl (M 456002). This was the original sink for the river but has since been modified by subsidence into the more recent cave beneath. A short distance to the west the river re-appears, flows north overground for 200m and sinks once more at Blackwater, next to the N18 (Gort to Ennis road), and then flows underground (at a depth of 30-40m below ground level) before emerging 1km to the west at Pollduagh Cave (M 445003). Between Blackwater and Pollduagh are two collapse dolines, each 13m deep: the Ladle is floored with boulders while the Churn is a vertical shaft leading directly into the underground Beagh/Gort River.

Pollduagh itself is a low, wide passage, the rectangular entrance having being modified by block collapse. Within a short distance of the entrance the roof dips below the water surface and the passage descends to a depth of 30m. Extensive solutionally formed shelving and hollows on the cave roof and walls demonstrate the sub-water table (phreatic) origin for the cave. Pollduagh and sections of cave are the remnants of what was formerly an extensive system of large river caves now largely obliterated by cavern collapse and by periodic glacial erosion and deposition in the area.

Surface-water karst-water interaction

Between the area of the Beagh/Gort sinking rivers and Caherglassaun Lough (M 417064), 8km to the west-north-west, the drainage is partly underground and partly on the surface. Lakes and other water bodies, uncharacteristic of karsts, are also common (Figure 13). Some of the water bodies are permanent or semi-permanent lakes, of which Coole Lough (M 430043) is one example (though it also functions as a huge swallow hole). Other lakes are turloughs (seasonal lakes), fed and emptied by internal springs and swallow holes or estavelles and located on zones of concentrated

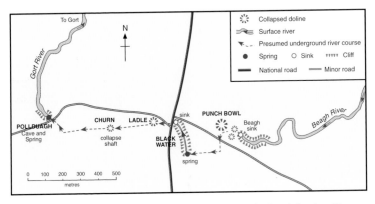

Figure 15: The course of the Beagh/Gort River between the Punch Bowl and its resurgence at Pollduagh.

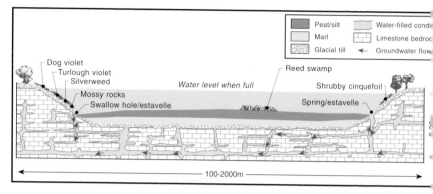

Figure 16: The characteristic topography, hydrology, sediments and vegetation of a typical turlough in the Gort-Kinvarra lowland. Adapted from Coxon, 1987.

groundwater flow. Turloughs are usually located in shallow hollows and have flat floors. They have a distinctive vegetational assemblage (Figure 16) associated with their peculiar hydrology. Garryland (M 416040), which is flooded for some 7-9 months of the year, is one of the best examples of a turlough in the Gort-Kinvarra area (Photo 15). Other water bodies show rises and falls in water level on a diurnal basis in response to tidal changes in water level in the outlet spring zone. The small Hawkhill Lough (M 412023) is some 9km from the sea and shows this effect, as does the much larger Caherglassaun Lough (M 415064), which in dry summer conditions and may appear

Photo 15: Garryland Turlough. *The numerous small collapsed dolines in the floor of the turlough indicate the highly karstified nature of the limestone bedrock. Photo: David Drew.*

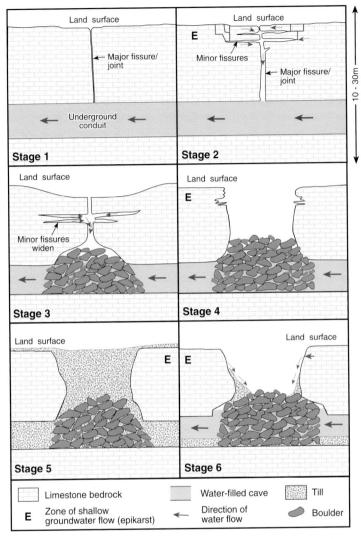

Figure 17: Hypothetical six-stage development sequence for the collapse dolines (karst windows) associated with the underground course of the Gort River and its underground tributaries. Stage 1: intact underground conduit with vertical major fissure; Stage 2: major fissure widens and minor fissures (horizontal) form; Stage 3: minor fissures widen, causing some collapse of bedrock into the underground conduit; Stage 4: karst window is fully open with collapsed bedrock filling underground conduit; Stage 5: till fills karst window and blocks groundwater flow; Stage 6: till is carried away by groundwater. Moran's Cave would be at Stage 3 of development, the Churn at Stage 3-4, the doline at Pollnadirk at Stage 5-6, and Pollbehan and Poulaloughabo at Stage 6 (see Figure 13 on page 41 for locations).

and disappear on a twice daily basis. One reason for these fluctuations is the backing up of fresh water inland as the rise and fall in sea level at the coast makes it difficult for fresh water to discharge from the springs in the inter-tidal zone.

Wholly underground drainage

The area between Caherglassaun Lough and Galway Bay is almost devoid of surface water and the landscape is flat and featureless – areas of limestone pavement alternate with till-covered mounds and ridges. The most distinctive landforms are the large enclosed depressions up to 15m in depth, 50m in diameter and often with vertical sides. The depressions lie in a line extending from Pollnapasty (M 414064), via Pollnadirk (M 400070), Moran's Cave (M 389076), Poulaloughabo (M 368080), Pollbehan (M 363082) to Quinn's Cave (M 355085) some 6.5km to the west-north-west (Figure 13, page 41). These dolines (termed 'karst windows') are the result of collapses into a major, water-filled karst conduit, of up to 25m in diameter, which conveys all of the underground drainage of the Gort area to the springs at Kinvarra (M 379103) and Corranroo Bay (M 325105). The way in which these karst windows may be formed is shown in Figure 17. Some collapses, Poulaloughabo (Photo 16) and Pollbehan for example, give direct access to the conduit, others are plugged with till (Pollnadirk), while in the case of Moran's Cave the subterranean collapse into the cave river has not yet been transmitted to the surface and hence no doline exists.

The conduit continues westwards to an ancient outlet in Galway Bay. However, most of the modern drainage short-circuits this route and flows to a series of springs on the foreshore between DunGuaire (Dungory) Castle and the town of Kinvarra. The springs are only apparent at low tide. The mean outflow from the springs at Kinvarra and Corranroo Bay is c. 10,000 litres per second but in high water conditions this flow may be exceeded 5-10 fold.

Access

As the karstic features described in this chapter are scattered over a wide area a circular route – starting and ending in Gort which will allow you to visit the main landforms – is suggested below.

Head south towards Limerick on the N18 for 2km, at a crossroads turn left (east) onto a minor road. After a further 500m the sink of the Beagh River and the Punch Bowl are on the left.

Return to the crossroads and continue to the west on the minor road. Just beyond the railway bridge, some 15m to the right off this road, is the rising of the same river (Cannahowna River) at Pollduagh.

Return to Gort and drive north on the N18 for 3.5km turning left (west) onto a minor road at Kiltartan (M 453058). Behind the church at Kiltartan is a rising of the Gort River at Polldeelin. The river sinks once more, some 600m downstream.

Photo 16: Poulaloughabo Cave *is a collapse into part of the underground course of the Gort River. Photo: David Drew.*

Continue on the minor road, turning west (left) towards Kinvarra after 2km (M 445079) then south (left again) at a crossroads (M 426080). After a further 2km Caherglassaun Lake is visible on the western (right-hand) side of the road.

Return to the crossroads and turn left for Kinvarra. In Kinvarra Village, turn right onto the N67 and park in the car park at M 383106. At low tide the series of inter-tidal springs are visible over a 600m-stretch of foreshore to the west of DunGuaire Castle.

Close to the Castle turn inland (left from the car park) on the R347 and continue to Ardrahan. At Ardrahan turn south (right) onto the N18, Lissatunny (M 470078) is 4km down this road. At Lissatunny turn onto a minor road to the south-east (left) towards the Ballylee Interpretative Centre (approximately 2km) where there is a car park (at M 482060). The Centre is adjacent to the T-sinks of the Ballylee River. To the north of the Centre a very narrow road leads, via Dromorehill, past the southern shore of Lough Coy and thence, after 1km, to the junction with the N66 (at M 494067) at Ballynabucky. Turn south (right), after 6km you will be back in Gort.

GLOSSARY

Anastomoses. A network of small (50-200mm diameter) tubes developed by solutional erosion in a bedding plane or fissure in the limestone by slowly-moving water. They represent an early stage in the development of an underground karst drainage system. Eventually one channel becomes enlarged preferentially and the remaining anastomosing channels are abandoned but may be preserved, particularly in the roof of a cave.

Calcite. A mineral composed of calcium carbonate which is the major constituent of limestone rock.

Chert. A siliceous mineral, similar to flint, and commonly occurring as lenses or nodules in the bedding planes of limestone strata. The chert is insoluble and may act as a barrier to the downward percolation of rainwater through the rock and so act as a focus for cave development in the bedding planes.

Clint. The blocks of limestone into which limestone pavements are divided by enlarged joints (grikes).

Doline. A small to medium sized closed depression a few metres to a few hundreds of metres in diameter. Dolines are formed by slow, concentrated solutional removal of rock in an area from the surface downwards or by the collapse of overlying rock into a cave or chamber beneath (collapse doline). Dolines function as funnels, allowing rainwater runoff to enter the karstic aquifer.

Dry valley. A valley which no longer contains a stream, the waters that eroded the valley now having developed underground routes.

Estavelle. A feature which may function as a swallow hole or as a spring depending upon the hydraulic conditions prevailing at a particular time. Poljes and turloughs may be filled and emptied via estavelles.

Grike. A joint, vertical or near-vertical, at the surface, which has been widened by solutional erosion. Grikes are usually well exposed on limestone pavements.

Half tube. The remnant, in the roof of a cave passage, of an old conduit, originally of approximately circular or elliptical cross-section, which has been partly destroyed by subsequent enlargement and/or collapse of the cave passage.

Kamenitza. Basins or pits developed on exposed limestone surfaces by the solutional action of standing water. They range in diameter from a few centimetres to a few metres and in depth from 1 to 100cm.

Karren (karrenfields). Small (millimetres to a few metres) solutional channels, hollows or enlarged fissures on the surface of the rock. Extensive exposures of bedrock with such features are termed karrenfields.

Karst (karstic). An area of limestone or other highly soluble rock, in which the landforms are of dominantly solutional origin and in which the drainage is underground in solutionally enlarged fissures and conduits.

Karstification. The progressive development of karstic landforms and karstic functioning (surface and underground) in an area. Gradations exist between slightly karstified areas, in which other geomorphic processes are important and a distinctive karstic hydrogeology has not fully developed, and wholly karstified areas (holokarst).

Limestone pavement. An area of bare exposed limestone which is relatively unmodified by mechanical or chemical weathering. Limestone pavements are thought to be the product of the removal of soil and weathered rock by glacial erosion and are therefore found only in areas that were glaciated in recent times.

Phreatic (cave). A cave that is developing or (if abandoned) was developed in the saturated zone and in which the passages are/were therefore completely water-filled. Passage cross-sections are commonly circular or elliptical, reflecting the fact that solution of the limestone can take place on all the rock surfaces of the passage.

Polje. A large, relatively flat-floored enclosed depression bounded by steep sides, with a floor area of $1km^2$ to several hundred square kilometres. Commonly, sediments blanket some or all of the floor.

Rendzina. A thin soil with a high organic content, typical of limestone outcrops.

Speleothem. Cave deposit formed by the precipitation of calcite from flowing or dripping water.

Swallow hole/sink. The point at which a surface stream sinks underground.

Turlough. A shallow seasonal lake in a karst environment, water-filled during the wetter part of the year and dry for several months. Turloughs are widespread on the limestone lowlands of the west of Ireland. The term derives from the Irish for 'dry lake'.

Uranium series dating. Determination of age based on measuring the relative amounts of naturally occurring uranium and its radioactive decay products, in this instance speleothems.

Uvala. A complex enclosed depression where dolines have developed within dolines. In plan view uvalas are usually irregular in form.

Vadose cave. A cave that is being or was developed in the unsaturated (vadose) zone of a karstic aquifer in which gravity flow is dominant. Such cave passages often take the form of a canyon or trench with the stream occupying the lowest part of the canyon in the same manner as a surface stream in a gorge. Solutional erosion is confined to those rock surfaces in contact with the stream.

BIBLIOGRAPHY

Coxon, C.E. (1987) 'The spatial distribution of turloughs', *Irish Geography*, 20, pp. 11-23.

Coxon, C. and Reynolds, R. (1987) *Turloughs*, Resource Source Guide No 10. Dublin: Environment Awareness Bureau.

Drew, D.P. (1973) 'A preliminary study of the geomorphology of the Aillwee area, Central Burren, County Clare', *Proceedings of the University of Bristol Speleological Society*, 13, 2, pp. 227-44.

Drew, D.P. (1975) 'Landforms of the Burren, County Clare', *Geographical Viewpoint*, 4, pp. 21-38.

Drew, D.P. (1988) 'The hydrology of the upper Fergus River catchment, County Clare', *Proceedings of the University of Bristol Speleological Society*, 18, 2, pp. 265-77.

Drew, D.P. (1990) 'The hydrology of the Burren', *Irish Geography*, 23, 2, pp. 69-89.

Drew D.P. and Cohen J. (1980) 'Geomorphology and sediments of Aillwee Cave, County Clare, Ireland', *Proceedings of the University of Bristol Speleological Society*, 15, 3, pp. 227-40.

Drew, D.P. and Daly, D. (1993) *Groundwater and Karstification in Mid Galway, South Mayo and North Clare*. Report Series 93/3. Dublin: Geological Survey Of Ireland.

Farrington, A. (1965) 'The last glaciation of the Burren', *Proceedings of the Royal Irish Academy*, 64B, pp. 33-9.

Finch, T.F. (1971) *Soils of County Clare*. Dublin: An Foras Taluntais.

Lundberg, J. (1977) 'Karren of the littoral zone, Burren district, County Clare, Ireland' in Ford, T. (ed) *Proceedings of the Seventh International Speleological Congress*, Sheffield, pp. 291-3.

Nelson, C.E. and Walsh, W. (1991) *The Burren*. Aberystwyth: Boethius Press.

O'Connell, J.W. and Korff, A. (1991) *The Book of the Burren*. Galway: Tir Eolas.

O'Connell, M. (ed) (1994) *The Burren*. Irish Association for Quaternary Studies Field Guide No. 18. Dublin: International Association for Quaternary Studies.

Office of Public Works (1997) *Investigation on the Flooding Problems in the Gort Ardrahan area of South Galway*. Dublin: Office of Public Works.

Self, C. (ed) (1981) *Caves of County Clare*. Somerset: Castle Cary.

Sherwood, D. (1992) 'Limestone pavement areas, Burren region', *Geographical Viewpoint*, 20, pp. 98-103.

Simms, M. (1990) 'Phytokarst and phytokarren in Ireland', *Cave Science*, 17, 3, pp. 131-3.

Sweeting, M.M. (1953) 'The enclosed depression of Carran, County Clare', *Irish Geography*, 2, 5, pp. 218-24.

Tratman, E.K. (ed) (1968) *The Caves of North-west Clare, Ireland.* Newton Abbot: David and Charles.

Trudgill, S. (1976) 'The erosion of limestones under soil and the long term stability of soil-vegetation systems on limestones, County Clare', *Earth Surface Processes*, 1, 1, pp. 31-42.

Williams, P. (1966) 'Limestone pavements with special reference to western Ireland', *Transactions of the Institute of British Geographers*, 40, pp. 155-72.

Williams, P. (1970) 'Limestone morphology in Ireland' in Stephens, N. and Glasscock, R. (eds) *Irish Geographical Studies.* Belfast: Queen's University, pp. 105-24.